Kids Learn!

Getting Ready for

2nd Grade

Contributing Author

Jodene Smith, M.A.

Publishing Credits

Conni Medina, M.A.Ed., *Managing Editor*; Robin Erickson, *Production Director*; Lee Aucoin, *Creative Director*; Timothy J. Bradley, *Illustration Manager*; Aubrie Nielsen, M.S.Ed., *Senior Editor*; Caroline Gasca, M.S.Ed., *Editor*; Melina Sánchez, *Assistant Editor*; Marissa Rodriguez, *Designer*; Stephanie Reid, *Photo Editor*; Rachelle Cracchiolo, M.S.Ed., *Publisher*

Image Credits

p. 89 iStockphoto; All other images Shutterstock.

Teacher Created Materials

5301 Oceanus Drive
Huntington Beach, CA 92649-1030
http://www.tcmpub.com
ISBN 978-1-4333-2534-2
© 2014 Teacher Created Materials, Inc.

Table of Contents

Introduction

Weekly Activities for Students

Appendices

Índice de materias

Introducción

Actividades semanales para estudiantes

Apéndices

© *Teacher Created Materials*

#13534—*Kids Learn! Getting Ready for 2nd Grade*

3

Welcome to Kids Learn!

Dear Family,

Welcome to *Kids Learn! Getting Ready for 2nd Grade*. Second grade will be an exciting year, with plenty of new learning opportunities. For example, your child will have the chance to explore a wider variety of reading material as well as gain exposure to many new math concepts, such as place value and money! Interesting new topics in science and social studies will keep students engaged in lessons at school as well.

Kids Learn! was designed to help solidify the concepts your child learned in first grade and help your child prepare for the year ahead. The activities are based on the *Common Core State Standards* and provide practice with essential skills for the grade level. Keeping the skills your child learned in first grade sharp while on break from school will help his or her second grade year get off to a great start.

Keep these tips in mind as you work with your child through the *Kids Learn!* book:

- Set aside **a specific time each day** to work on the activities.

- **Complete one language arts and one mathematics page** each time your child works in the book rather than an entire week's worth of activity pages at one time.

- Keep all **practice sessions with your child positive and constructive.** If the mood becomes tense or if either of you gets frustrated, set the book aside and find another time for your child to practice.

- **Help your child understand each activity** and provide guidance as he or she works through each page.

- Discuss the activities with your child. **Look for the *Talk About It!* icon** at the end of each activity.

- Encourage your child to do his or her best work and **compliment the effort that goes into learning.** Celebrate the completion of the activities by filling in the certificate at the end of the book and displaying it in a special place.

Enjoy the time learning with your child during his or her vacation from school. Second grade will be here before you know it!

Bienvenidos a Kids Learn!

Querida familia:

Bienvenidos a *Kids Learn! Getting Ready for 2nd Grade*. El segundo grado será un año emocionante con bastantes nuevas oportunidades de aprender. Por ejemplo, ¡su hijo tendrá la oportunidad de explorar una más amplia variedad de material de lectura así como de familiarizarse con muchos nuevos conceptos matemáticos, como el valor de posición y el dinero! Nuevos temas interesantes en ciencias y estudios sociales también mantendrán a los estudiantes involucrados en las lecciones escolares.

Kids Learn! fue diseñado para ayudar a consolidar los conceptos que su hijo aprendió en el primer grado y para ayudar a su hijo a prepararse para el año que viene. Las actividades están basadas en los Estándares comunes del estado (*Common Core State Standards*) y proveen práctica con las destrezas esenciales para el nivel de ese grado. Mantener a punto las destrezas que su hijo aprendió en el primer grado mientras su hijo está de descanso de la escuela ayudará a que el año del segundo grado comience de gran manera.

Tenga en cuenta estos consejos mientras completa junto con su hijo el libro *Kids Learn!*:

- Reserve un **tiempo específico todos los días** para trabajar en las actividades.
- **Complete una página de artes del lenguaje y una página de matemáticas** cada vez que su hijo trabaje con el libro, en lugar de completar al mismo tiempo las páginas de actividades que se completarían en una semana.
- Mantenga todas las **sesiones de práctica con su hijo positivas y constructivas.** Si el estado de ánimo se pone tenso, o usted o su hijo se frustran, ponga el libro a un lado y busque otro momento para practicar.
- **Ayude a su hijo a entender cada actividad** y guíelo mientras completa cada página.
- Converse con su hijo acerca de las actividades. **Busque el símbolo de** *¡Hablar de ello!* al final de cada actividad.
- Anime a su hijo a que haga su mejor esfuerzo y **elogie el empeño que se dedica cuando se aprende.** Celebre la terminación de todas las actividades llenando el certificado que se encuentra al final del libro y poniéndolo en un lugar especial.

Disfrute el tiempo en el que aprende con su hijo durante sus vacaciones de la escuela. ¡El segundo grado llegará antes de que se dé cuenta!

Top 10 Things Your Second Grader Will Need to Know

1. **Word strategies** for reading words (e.g., short and long vowels, common vowel teams—*ea*, *ee*, and *ie*)

2. **Literature** from around the world (e.g., folktales, fairy tales, classic myths)

3. **Writing** from a variety of genres (e.g., letters, journal entries, book reports)

4. **Addition and subtraction** within 20

5. **Place value**

6. **Time and money**

7. **Life cycles** of plants and animals

8. Materials in **solid, liquid, and gas forms**

9. **Time lines and ancestors,** as well as important heroes

10. Different **types of governments in the country**

#13534—Kids Learn! Getting Ready for 2nd Grade

Las 10 cosas que su hijo de segundo grado debe saber

1. **Estrategias para la lectura de las palabras** (p. ej. vocales cortas y largas, grupos de vocales más comunes *ea*, *ee*, *ie*)

2. **Literatura** de todo el mundo (p. ej. cuentos populares, cuentos de hadas, mitos clásicos)

3. **Escritura** en diversos géneros (p. ej. cartas, entradas de diario, informes de libros)

4. **Suma y resta** de 1 a 20

5. **Valor posicional**

6. **Tiempo y dinero**

7. **Ciclos vitales** de plantas y animales

8. Materiales en **estado sólido, líquido y gaseoso**

9. **Líneas de tiempo y antepasados**, así como héroes importantes

10. Diferentes **tipos de gobierno en el país**

#13534—Kids Learn! Getting Ready for 2nd Grade

7

Things to Do at Home

To Develop Healthy Habits

- Be firm and consistent about bedtime every night. Use a clock or timer to signal the start of the bedtime routine and make sure to turn off the TV and other electronics at least 30 minutes before bedtime.

- Set aside a consistent time for homework each day. Designate a quiet area for your child to work and provide assistance only when needed.

- Work together with your child to create a daily schedule, including homework time, playtime, chores, activities, and bedtime. Post the schedule in a visible place as a reference for you and your child.

SCHEDULE

4:00	Snack
4:30	Piano practice
5:00	Set the table, feed the dog
5:30	Dinner
6:30	Homework and reading time
7:15	Free time (after homework)
7:45	Get ready for bed

To Practice Reading

- Encourage your child to read words he or she knows on food packages or in magazines, newspapers, or advertisements. Allow your child to cut out these words and glue them to a sheet of paper, thereby creating a personal dictionary.

- Write a list of one-step directions for your child to complete over the course of the day—for example, *Brush your teeth*. Reward your child with a sticker or smiley face next to each item that he or she reads and completes.

- Once your child has finished reading a book, have your child retell the story in his or her own words. If necessary, have your child use the pictures in the book as clues about what happened.

To Practice Writing

- Ask your child to write and illustrate a story for a younger sibling or friend. Encourage your child to include a beginning, a middle, and an end.

- Have your child write your grocery or to-do list for you. Encourage your child to sound out each word as he or she writes it.

- Provide your child with sticky notes, index cards, or small sheets of paper. Have him or her label items around the house by writing the name of the object on the sticky note and attaching it to the object.

Shopping List
eggs
milk
pasta
juice
bananas
apples

To Practice Math

- Place 15–20 coins of varying denominations in a bag. Have your child pull out a handful of coins and help him or her sort and count the money.

- Ask your child to determine how many pairs of shoes there are in your house by counting by two. Encourage your child to find other things that can be counted by two, such as eyes, mittens, and socks.

- Create a schedule of events for the day (breakfast, school, playtime, bedtime) and write the corresponding times next to each event. Encourage your child to periodically check the time on a clock and check the schedule for upcoming events.

#13534—Kids Learn! Getting Ready for 2nd Grade

9

Cosas para hacer en casa

Para desarrollar hábitos saludables

- Sea firme y constante sobre la hora de dormir todas las noches. Use un reloj o un temporizador para indicar el comienzo de la rutina de la hora de dormir y asegúrese de apagar la televisión y otros aparatos electrónicos al menos 30 minutos antes de la hora de dormir.

- Aparte un tiempo determinado todos los días para hacer la tarea. Designe un área silenciosa para que su hijo trabaje y ayúdelo sólo cuando sea necesario.

- Trabaje con su hijo para crear un horario que incluya tiempo para la tarea, para jugar, para los quehaceres, para las actividades y para la hora de dormir. Ponga el horario en un lugar visible como referencia para usted y para su hijo.

HORARIO

4:00	Refrigerio
4:30	Práctica de piano
5:00	Poner la mesa, darle de comer al perro
5:30	Cena
6:30	Tarea y hora de leer
7:15	Tiempo libre (después de la tarea)
7:45	Prepararse para dormir

Para practicar la lectura

- Anime a su hijo a que lea palabras que sabe en paquetes de comida o en revistas, periódicos o anuncios. Deje que su hijo recorte estas palabras y que las pegue en una hoja de papel, creando así un diccionario personal.

- Escriba una lista de instrucciones de un solo paso para que su hijo las complete a través del día; por ejemplo, *Cepíllate los dientes.* Recompense a su hijo con una calcomanía o una carita feliz al lado de cada instrucción que lea y complete.

- En cuanto su hijo haya terminado de leer un libro, pídale que vuelva a contar la historia en sus propias palabras. Si es necesario, haga que su hijo use imágenes del libro como pistas sobre lo que ocurrió.

Para practicar la escritura

- Pida a su hijo que escriba e ilustre una historia para un hermano menor o un amigo. Anime a su hijo a incluir el principio, el desarrollo y el final.

- Haga que su hijo le escriba la lista del mandado o lista de cosas que hacer. Anime a su hijo a deletrear la palabra en voz alta mientras la escribe.

- Provea a su hijo con notas adhesivas, fichas u hojas de papel pequeñas. Haga que etiquete objetos que hay en la casa escribiendo el nombre del objeto en la nota adhesiva y pegándola al objeto.

Lista de compras
huevos
leche
pasta
jugo
plátanos
manzanas

Para practicar las matemáticas

- Coloque en una bolsa de 15 a 20 monedas de diferentes denominaciones. Haga que su hijo saque un puñado de monedas y ayúdelo a clasificar y contar el dinero.

- Pida a su hijo que determine cuántos pares de zapatos hay en su casa contando de dos en dos. Anime a su hijo a encontrar otras cosas que puedan contarse de dos en dos, como ojos, guantes y calcetines.

- Cree un horario de actividades para el día (desayuno, escuela, hora de juegos, hora de dormir) y escriba las horas correspondientes al lado de cada actividad. Anime a su hijo a que revise periódicamente la hora en un reloj y a que revise el horario para actividades próximas.

Things to Do in the Community

To Develop Good Citizenship

- Have a discussion with your child about what good citizenship means, including the rights and responsibilities of citizens. Help your child think of someone in your community who exhibits good citizenship and have your child write a thank-you note to that person.

- Visit your local library and check out a book on recycling. Discuss the importance of recycling with your child and make a list of items that can be recycled in your community.

- Volunteer to help serve a meal at a homeless shelter with your child and talk about the importance of helping others who are in need.

To Practice Reading

- Attend story time at your local library. Ask your child questions about the story that was read and have him or her retell the story to you on your way home.

- Write directions to get from your house to a local store (e.g., *Turn left on Main Street*). The next time you go to the store, ask your child to read the directions aloud and help you navigate to your destination.

- Practice reading movie posters advertising upcoming movies. Encourage your child to find the titles of the movies and the dates when they will be released in theaters.

To Practice Writing

- Have your child write about a movie or TV show that he or she has seen. Encourage your child to include at least one sentence about the beginning, the middle, and the end of the movie or show.

- After going on an outing or attending a community event, have your child write about it. Ask him or her to include the sequence of events and how he or she felt about the experience.

- Encourage your child to try something new, such as a different food at a restaurant or a new piece of equipment at the playground. Have your child write about his or her experience and whether he or she would try it again.

To Practice Math

- Encourage your child to practice reading the time on any clocks you pass by in the community. You may also have your child look for the temperature, which is often displayed in many locations.

- Encourage your child to find things in the community that are about as long as an inch, a foot, and a yard. If possible, bring a measuring tape along to verify the actual lengths.

- Have your child make up addition and subtraction problems while you are out in the community. For example, *If there are ten cars in the parking lot and three cars leave and then one enters, how many cars are now in the parking lot?*

Cosas para hacer en la comunidad

Para ser un buen ciudadano

- Comente con su hijo sobre qué quiere decir ser un buen ciudadano, incluyendo los derechos y las responsabilidades de los ciudadanos. Ayude a su hijo a pensar en alguien de su comunidad que demuestra ser un buen ciudadano y haga que su hijo escriba una nota de agradecimento a esa persona.

- Visiten su biblioteca local y saquen prestado un libro sobre el reciclaje. Hable con su hijo sobre la importancia del reciclaje y hagan una lista de objetos que pueden ser reciclados en su comunidad.

- Ofrézcanse como voluntarios para ayudar a servir comida en un albergue para indigentes y hablen sobre la importancia de ayudar a aquellos que están necesitados.

Para practicar la lectura

- Asista a la hora de lectura de su biblioteca local. Haga preguntas a su hijo sobre la historia que se leyó y pídale que le vuelva a contar la historia de regreso a casa.

- Escriba indicaciones para ir desde su casa a una tienda local (ej. *Dobla a la izquierda en Main Street*). La próxima vez que vayan a la tienda, pida a su hijo que lea las indicaciones en voz alta y que le ayude a llegar a su destino.

- Practiquen leer carteles que promocionan películas que se estrenarán pronto. Anime a su hijo a encontrar los títulos de las películas y las fechas de cuándo se estrenan en los cines.

Para practicar la escritura

- Haga que su hijo escriba sobre una película o programa de televisión que haya visto. Anime a su hijo a que incluya al menos una oración sobre el principio, el desarrollo y el final de la película o el programa.

- Después de salir a pasear o de asistir a un evento en su comunidad, haga que su hijo escriba sobre él. Pídale que incluya el orden de las actividades y cómo se sintió después de esta experiencia.

- Anime a su hijo a probar algo nuevo, como una comida diferente en un restaurante, o un nuevo juego en el parque. Pida a su hijo que escriba sobre su experiencia y si lo haría otra vez.

Para practicar las matemáticas

- Anime a su hijo a que practique leer la hora en cualquier reloj que vea en la comunidad. También puede pedirle a su hijo que busque la temperatura, que a menudo se muestra en muchos lugares.

- Anime a su hijo a buscar cosas en la comunidad que sean más o menos del largo de una pulgada, de un pie y de una yarda. Si es posible, lleve consigo una cinta de medir para verificar las longitudes precisas.

- Haga que su hijo invente problemas de sumas y restas mientras andan por la comunidad. Por ejemplo, *Si hay diez automóviles en el estacionamiento y tres automóviles se van y luego uno entra, ¿cuántos automóviles hay ahora en el estacionamiento?*

Suggested Vacation Reading
Lectura sugerida para las vacaciones

These books are recommended for students in first and second grades. Most, if not all, of these books are available at your local library or bookstore. Encourage your child to read daily and record his or her reading progress on the Vacation Reading Log on page 17.

Estos libros son recomendados para estudiantes de primero y segundo grado. La mayoría, si no todos estos libros, están disponibles en su biblioteca o librería local. Anime a su hijo a que lea diariamente y registre el progreso de su lectura en el Registro de lectura de las vacaciones en la página 17.

Fiction

Mercy Watson to the Rescue by Kate DiCamillo
These Hands by Margaret H. Mason
Small Pig by Arnold Lobel
Tacky the Penguin by Helen Lester
Bear Snores On by Karma Wilson
Lin Yi's Lantern by Brenda Williams and
    Benjamin Lacombe
Harry the Dirty Dog by Gene Zion
Boo's Dinosaur by Betsy Byars
Little Bear by Else Holmelund Minarik and
    Maurice Sendak
Each Kindness by Jacqueline Woodson

Nonfiction

Horses Up Close by Christopher Blazeman
Meet the Dogs of Bedlam Farm by Jon Katz
Helen's Big World: The Life of Helen Keller
    by Doreen Rappaport
Rosie: A Visiting Dog's Story by Stephanie Calmenson
Where Butterflies Grow by Joanne Ryder
A River of Words: The Story of William Carlos Williams
    by Jen Bryant
Picasso and Minou by P. I. Maltbie
Teammates by Peter Golenbock
Castle: Medieval Days and Knights by Kyle Olmon
Carolina's Story: Sea Turtles Get Sick Too!
    by Donna Rathmell

Vacation Reading Log
Registro de lectura de las vacaciones

Help your child complete this reading log to keep track of his or her vacation reading.
Ayude a su hijo a completar este registro de lectura para llevar la cuenta de su lectura durante las vacaciones.

Date *Fecha*	Title *Título*	Number of pages *Número de páginas*

Websites and Apps for Parents and Kids
Páginas web y aplicaciones para padres y niños

Language Arts Websites

Reading Rockets
http://www.readingrockets.org
Information, activities, and advice for parents

Magic Keys
http://www.magickeys.com/books
Collection of online children's storybooks divided into sections for young children, older children, and young adults

Read, Write, Think
http://www.readwritethink.org/parent -afterschool-resources
Student materials that support literacy learning in the K-12 classroom

International Children's Digital Library
http://en.childrenslibrary.org
Online database of eBooks organized by age, reading level, language, genre, or interest

Starfall
http://www.starfall.com
Phonics program that introduces letter names and sounds and also contains a series of interactive reading material for beginning readers

Mathematics Websites

PBS Early Math
http://www.pbs.org/parents/education/math
Math-based activities and developmental milestones for children 6-9 years old

Sheppard Software
http://www.sheppardsoftware.com/math.htm
Collection of interactive math games covering a large variety of topics

SoftSchools.com
http://www.softschools.com/math
Math concepts, tips, games, and activity sheets

Figure This! Math Challenges for Families
http://www.figurethis.org
Math problems to challenge families

Education.com
http://www.education.com/activity/math/
Suggestions for math games to make and play at home

En español

Mundo Latino
http://www.mundolatino.org
Base de datos extensiva para hispanohablantes con enlaces a diferentes temas, juegos educativos y revistas en la red

StoryPlace
http://www.storyplace.org/sp/storyplace.asp
Una biblioteca digital con páginas llenas de cuentos para niños, jóvenes y adultos

¡Colorín Colorado!
http://www.colorincolorado.org
Información, actividades y consejos para padres y maestros de estudiantes que hablan español

Aplicaciones Didácticas
http://www.aplicaciones.info/lectura/lectura .htm#peques
Base de datos de cuentos cortos y preguntas de comprensión correspondientes

Cibercuentos
http://www.cibercuentos.org
Una serie de cuentos interactivos en español para las edades de 3-8 años

Fun Educational Apps

Kids Learn Sight Words Games
Teacher Created Materials, Inc.
Familiar games such as hangman, tic-tac-toe, word search, and word match provide fun and engaging practice with sight words

Coin Math
Recession Apps
Learn to recognize, count, add, and make change using U.S. coins

JumpStart Jetpack
Knowledge Adventure
Earn points by collecting correct answers and zapping incorrect answers to language arts and math questions

KickBox
MIND Research Institute
Visual problem solving at seven progressive levels

Weekly Activities for Students

Actividades semanales para estudiantes

#13534—Kids Learn! Getting Ready for 2nd Grade

19

Long or Short?

Directions: Decide whether the vowel sound is short or long. Fill in the correct bubble.

Instrucciones: Decide si el sonido de la vocal es corto o largo. Rellena el círculo correcto.

1.
○ short   ◉ long

2.
◉ short   ○ long

3.
○ short   ◉ long

4.
○ short   ◉ long

5.
◉ short   ○ long

6.
◉ short   ○ long

7.
○ short   ◉ long

8.
○ short   ◉ long

9.
◉ short   ○ long

Talk About It!
¡Hablar de ello!

What is another word with a long vowel sound?

¿Cuál es otra palabra con un sonido de vocal larga?

Count Big Numbers

Directions: Count by one. Write the missing numbers.

Instrucciones: Cuenta de a uno. Escribe los números que faltan.

1. 103, __104__, _____, _____, _____,

_____, _____, _____, _____

2. _____, _____, _____, 101, _____,

_____, _____, _____, _____

3. _____, 117, _____, _____, _____,

_____, _____, _____

4. _____, _____, _____, _____,

119, _____, _____, _____, _____

5. _____, _____, 107, _____, _____,

_____, _____, _____, _____

6. _____, _____, 112, _____, _____,

_____, _____, _____, _____

Talk About It!
¡Hablar de ello!

How did you know which number to write in each blank?

¿Cómo supiste cuál número escribir en cada espacio en blanco?

A Day at the Beach

Directions: Read the passage. Answer the questions.

Instrucciones: Lee el pasaje. Contesta las preguntas.

The beach is a great place to visit. There are many things to do there.

Some people like to sit on the sand at the beach. They like to read a book or take a nap. Building sandcastles is fun for other people. They use sand, shovels, and pails.

Some people like to pick up seashells and sand dollars at the beach. You can find them in sand or water.

Many people like to play in the water. They like to splash in the waves. Some people like to go surfing.

Not everyone likes to do exactly the same things at the beach. But one thing is for sure—no matter what you do at the beach, you are sure to have a fun day!

1. What is this passage about?
- (A) people
- (B) things to do at the beach
- (C) things you need for surfing
- (D) how to build sandcastles

2. Which is not needed to make a sandcastle?
- (A) a shovel
- (B) a board
- (C) sand
- (D) a pail

Where in the passage did you find the answer to each question?

¿Dónde en el pasaje encontraste la respuesta a cada pregunta?

Comparing Numbers

Directions: Write the correct symbol in the circle to compare the numbers.

Instrucciones: Escribe el símbolo correcto en los círculos para comparar los números.

Tip

< is the symbol for *less than*
> is the symbol for *greater than*
= is the symbol for *equal*

< *es el símbolo para* menos que
> *es el símbolo para* más que
= *es el símbolo para* igual

1. 25 ⓥ> 17

5. 29 〇 29

2. 30 〇 34

6. 100 〇 12

3. 80 〇 75

7. 62 〇 65

4. 79 〇 97

8. 23 〇 32

Talk About It!
¡Hablar de ello!

Which is the greatest number on this page?

¿Cuál es el número más grande en esta página?

More Than One?

Directions: Circle the correct word for each picture. Write a sentence using one of the words you circled.

Instrucciones: *Encierra con un círculo la palabra correcta para cada imagen. Escribe una oración usando una de las palabras que circulaste.*

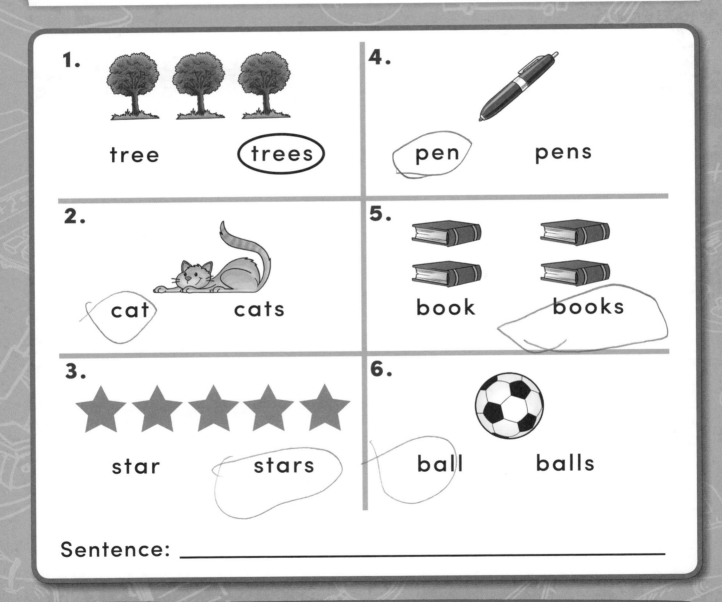

1. tree   (trees)

2. cat   cats

3. star   stars

4. pen   pens

5. book   books

6. ball   balls

Sentence: _____

**Talk About It!
¡Hablar de ello!**

A *plural* noun shows more than one. Which words are plural?

Un sustantivo plural *muestra más de uno. ¿Cuáles palabras son plurales?*

Name the Fraction

Directions: Use the Word Bank to name the shaded portion of each shape.

Instrucciones: Usa el Banco de palabras para nombrar la porción sombreada de cada figura.

Word Bank

one-half   one whole   one-quarter   one-third

1. _____one whole_____

2. _____

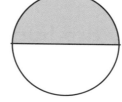

3. _____

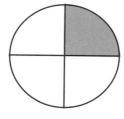

4. _____

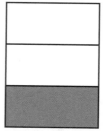

Talk About It!
¡Hablar de ello!

How do you know which fraction goes with each shape?

¿Cómo sabes cuál fracción va con cada figura?

Punctuation Station

Directions: Write a period, question mark, or exclamation point at the end of each sentence.

Instrucciones: *Escribe un punto, un signo de interrogación o un signo de exclamación al final de cada oración.*

1. I love going to the zoo _____!_____

2. We always take a snack along _____

3. We go see the elephants first _____

4. They are huge _____

5. The giraffes are my favorite animals _____

6. What is your favorite animal _____

7. It was a great day _____

8. When can we go again _____

Talk About It!
¡Hablar de ello!

Make up sentences that end with a period, a question mark, and an exclamation point.

Crea oraciones que terminen con un punto, un signo de interrogación o un signo de exclamación.

Picnic Time!

Directions: Draw pictures to solve the problem.

Instrucciones: Haz dibujos para resolver el problema.

Jamie's Plate   Jackson's Plate   Dad's Plate

Jamie and Jackson went on a picnic with Dad. Dad put 2 hot dogs on Jamie's plate and 2 hot dogs on Jackson's plate. He put one hot dog on his own plate. How many hot dogs were on the 3 plates?

_____

Talk About It!
¡Hablar de ello!

What addition number sentence could you make for this problem?
¿Qué oración numérica de sumas podrías hacer para este problema?

Reading Longer Words

Directions: Match each picture to the correct word.

Instrucciones: Une cada imagen a la palabra correcta.

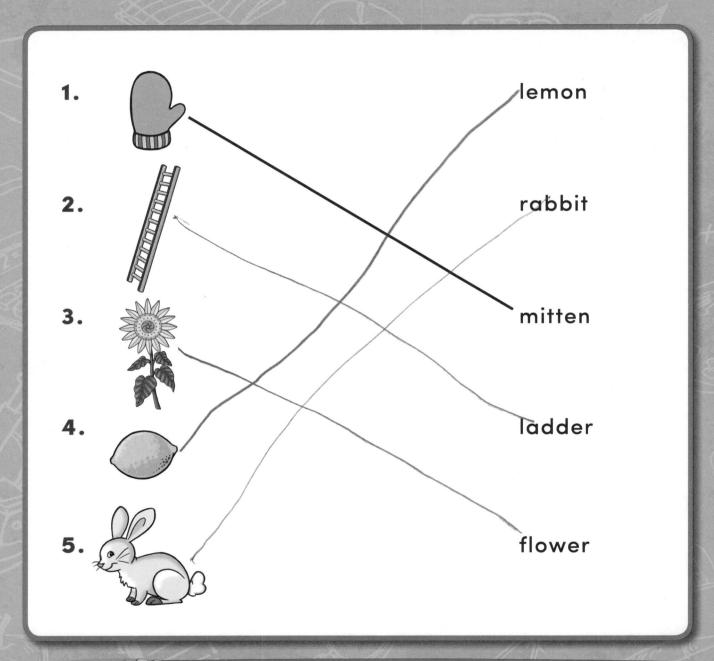

1.

2.

3.

4.

5.

lemon

rabbit

mitten

ladder

flower

Talk About It!
¡Hablar de ello!

How many syllables are in each word?

¿Cuántas sílabas hay en cada palabra?

Find the Missing Number

Directions: Solve the problems.

Instrucciones: Resuelve los problemas.

1. $4 + \underline{\quad 6 \quad} = 10$

5. $0 + \underline{\qquad} = 10$

2. $3 + \underline{\qquad} = 10$

6. $7 + \underline{\qquad} = 10$

3. $5 + \underline{\qquad} = 10$

7. $2 + \underline{\qquad} = 10$

4. $8 + \underline{\qquad} = 10$

8. $9 + \underline{\qquad} = 10$

Talk About It!
¡Hablar de ello!

How did you figure out which number should go in each blank?

¿Cómo te diste cuenta cuál número debe ir en cada espacio en blanco?

Favorite Movie

Directions: Write your opinion about a movie you have seen.

Instrucciones: *Escribe tu opinión sobre una película que has visto.*

#13534—Kids Learn! Getting Ready for 2nd Grade

© Teacher Created Materials

Spelling Words

Directions: Spell the word that names each picture.

Instrucciones: Deletrea la palabra que nombra cada imagen.

Short Vowels		Long Vowels	
1.	cub	5.	sqer
2.	tub	6.	
3.		7.	kiet
4.	can	8.	

Talk About It!
¡Hablar de ello!

Which letter at the end of a word can help make a long vowel sound?

¿Cuál letra al final de una palabra ayuda a hacer un sonido de vocal larga?

Comparing Numbers

Directions: Compare each pair of numbers. Choose the correct sign.

Instrucciones: Compara cada par de números. Escoge el símbolo correcto.

1. 87 ⃝ 78

  Ⓐ =

  Ⓑ >

  Ⓒ <

2. 34 ⃝ 45

  Ⓐ =

  Ⓑ >

  Ⓒ <

3. 19 ⃝ 14

  Ⓐ =

  Ⓑ >

  Ⓒ <

4. 39 ⃝ 78

  Ⓐ =

  Ⓑ >

  Ⓒ <

5. 72 ⃝ 72

  Ⓐ =

  Ⓑ >

  Ⓒ <

6. 91 ⃝ 55

  Ⓐ =

  Ⓑ >

  Ⓒ <

7. 23 ⃝ 57

  Ⓐ =

  Ⓑ >

  Ⓒ <

8. 72 ⃝ 20

  Ⓐ =

  Ⓑ >

  Ⓒ <

Talk About It! ¡Hablar de ello!

How do you know which number is greater in each set?

¿Cómo sabes cuál número es más grande en cada grupo?

Ways to Say It

Directions: Answer the questions below.

Instrucciones: Contesta las preguntas de abajo.

1. What is 1 ten and 5 ones?

   _____ 15

3. What is 1 ten and 1 one?

   _____

2. What is 1 ten and 6 ones?

   _____

4. What is 1 ten and 4 ones?

   _____

Write how many tens and ones each number has.

5. 19 = _____ ten and _____ ones

6. 13 = _____ ten and _____ ones

7. 18 = _____ ten and _____ ones

**Talk About It!
¡Hablar de ello!**

How many ones are in two tens?

¿Cuántos unos hay en dos decenas?

Numbers to 50

Directions: Write the numbers that are 10 more and 10 less.

Instrucciones: Escribe los números que son 10 más y 10 menos.

Ten Less		Ten More
1. _24_	34	_44_
2. _____	19	_____
3. _____	26	_____
4. _____	39	_____
5. _____	21	_____
6. _____	40	_____
7. _____	10	_____
8. _____	35	_____

10 more

10 less

3   13   23

**Talk About It!
¡Hablar de ello!**

How did you find the numbers that are 10 more and 10 less?

¿Cómo encontraste los números que son 10 más y 10 menos?

Word Sort

Directions: Write each word in the correct category.

Instrucciones: Escribe cada palabra en la categoría correcta.

Word Bank

computer	farmer	doctor	ruler
dancer	hammer	writer	saw
desk	mop	pilot	teacher

Tools or Things Used at Work	Workers
_____	_____
_____	_____
_____	_____
_____	_____
_____	_____
_____	_____

Talk About It! ¡Hablar de ello!

Name one more word for each category.

Nombra una palabra más para cada categoría.

Subtraction Word Problems

Directions: Write a number sentence to solve each story problem.

Instrucciones: Escribe una oración numérica para resolver cada problema de planteo.

1. Julia had 16 bows. She lost 10 bows. How many bows does she have left?

   _____ – _____ = _____ bows

2. There were 11 bees in a beehive. Then, 1 flew away. How many bees are left?

   _____ – _____ = _____ bees

3. Wendy had 13 dimes. She spent 5 of them. How many dimes does Wendy have left?

   _____ – _____ = _____ dimes

4. Han had 10 stickers. He gave 3 of them away. How many stickers does Han have left?

   _____ – _____ = _____ stickers

How do you solve subtraction problems?

¿Cómo resuelves problemas de resta?

Tracy's Trip

Directions: Read the passage, then answer the questions.

Instrucciones: Lee el pasaje, luego contesta las preguntas.

It was the night before Tracy's trip with her parents. Tracy could not wait. They were going to the mountains.

She began to pack for the trip. She packed warm clothes. She packed her camera, too. She wanted to take pictures. She packed her bird book. She hoped to see some birds.

Tracy thought she was ready. Then, she remembered her journal! She wanted to write each day about her trip.

Tracy lay on her bed. She was thinking of her trip. Soon, she drifted off to sleep.

1. Who is the main character?

   _____

2. Write two words that tell about the main character.

   _____

What do you think the girl will write about in her journal?

¿Sobre qué piensas que escribirá la niña en su diario?

Measure and Compare

Directions: Find the objects below. Use same-sized paper clips to measure each object.

Instrucciones: Encuentra los objetos de abajo. Usa sujetapapeles del mismo tamaño para medir cada objeto.

Tip

When you measure with paper clips, be sure to line up the paper clips correctly.
Cuando midas con sujetapapeles, asegúrate de alinear los sujetapapeles correctamente.

Correct
Correcto

Incorrect
Incorrecto

Objects to Measure	Length
1.	_____ paper clips
2.	_____ paper clips
3.	_____ paper clips
4.	_____ paper clips
5.	_____ paper clips

Talk About It!
¡Hablar de ello!

Which object is the shortest? Which is the longest?
¿Cuál objeto es el más pequeño? ¿Cuál es el más grande?

Word Round Up

Directions: Add endings to each base word to make new words. Be careful—not all the endings will work.

Instrucciones: Agrega terminaciones a cada palabra raíz para hacer nuevas palabras. Ten cuidado, no todas las terminaciones van a funcionar.

Word Endings

ed	s	ing	es

1. talk   talked, talks, talking

2. stay _____

3. box _____

4. fish _____

5. start _____

Read each word aloud.

Lee cada palabra en voz alta.

Number Detective

Directions: Solve each number sentence by filling in the missing number.

Instrucciones: Resuelve cada oración numérica al escribir el número que falta.

1. $2 + \boxed{2} = 4$

5. $\boxed{} - 1 = 6$

2. $\boxed{} - 2 = 8$

6. $3 + 2 = \boxed{}$

3. $14 + \boxed{} = 15$

7. $\boxed{} - 5 = 4$

4. $10 + \boxed{} = 20$

8. $8 + 2 = \boxed{}$

¡Talk About It! ¡Hablar de ello!

How did you decide which number should go in each box?

¿Cómo decidiste cuál número debía de ir en cada cuadro?

Bright and Early

Directions: Write what you did to get ready this morning.

Instrucciones: *Escribe qué hiciste para alistarte esta mañana.*

Vowel Sound Match

Directions: Match each underlined short- and long-vowel word with the word *short* or *long*.

Instrucciones: Une cada palabra de vocal corta y larga subrayada con la palabra larga o corta.

1. <u>Jan</u> gave the bag to <u>Jane</u>.

   short   long

2. The pilot has a <u>plan</u> for the <u>plane</u>.

   short   long

3. The <u>note</u> is <u>not</u> here.

   short   long

4. The <u>pin</u> is under the <u>pine</u> tree.

   short   long

5. The <u>pan</u> is by the <u>pane</u> of glass.

   short   long

Talk About It!
¡Hablar de ello!

Why doesn't the letter *e* make a sound in these long-vowel words?

¿Por qué la letra e no tiene sonido en estas palabras de vocal larga?

Drawing Tens and Ones

Directions: Draw a picture to represent each number in groups of tens and ones.

Instrucciones: Haz un dibujo para representar cada número en grupos de decenas y unidades.

1. 20 = __2__ tens 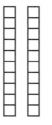 __0__ ones

2. 79 = ____ tens ____ ones

3. 45 = ____ tens ____ ones

4. 38 = ____ tens ____ ones

5. 61 = ____ tens ____ ones

What does *9 tens* equal? How do you know?

¿A qué equivale 9 decenas? ¿Cómo lo sabes?

A Frog's Life

Directions: Read the passage, then answer the questions.

Instrucciones: Lee el pasaje, luego contesta las preguntas

A mother frog lives in a pond. She is ready to lay eggs. She lays eggs in the water. Each egg can become a frog. When the eggs hatch, tadpoles come out. A tadpole looks like a little fish. The tadpole grows. It looks like a fish with two legs. Then it grows two more legs. Now it has four legs. It looks more like a frog. Each young frog becomes an adult frog. Then the cycle starts again.

1. What does a tadpole look like?

- (A) a leg
- (B) a fish
- (C) an egg
- (D) water

2. What does this story tell about?

- (A) tadpoles
- (B) the life cycle of a frog
- (C) mother frogs
- (D) frog eggs

Talk About It!
¡Hablar de ello!

Where in the passage did you find the answer to each question?

¿Dónde en el pasaje encontraste la respuesta a cada pregunta?

Fact Families

Directions: Complete each fact family by writing one addition and one subtraction number sentence.

Instrucciones: Completa cada familia de operaciones al escribir una oración numérica de sumas y una de restas.

1. $6 + 9 = 15$

$15 - 9 = 6$

$\underline{9} + \underline{6} = \underline{15}$

$\underline{15} - \underline{6} = \underline{9}$

2. $8 + 5 = 13$

$13 - 5 = 8$

$\underline{5} + \underline{8} = \underline{13}$

$\underline{5} - \underline{13} = \underline{8}$

3. $4 + 3 = 7$

$7 - 3 = 4$

$\underline{3} + \underline{4} = \underline{7}$

$\underline{7} - \underline{3} = \underline{4}$

4. $7 + 9 = 16$

$16 - 9 = 7$

$\underline{9} + \underline{7} = \underline{16}$

$\underline{9} - \underline{16} = \underline{7}$

Talk About It! ¡Hablar de ello!

Why is there only one subtraction and one addition number sentence for the fact family with the numbers 5, 5, and 10?

¿Por qué hay sólo una oración numérica de restas y una de sumas para la familia de operaciones con los números 5, 5 y 10?

Adjectives at Work

Directions: Circle each adjective in the sentences. Then, underline the noun it describes. There may be more than one adjective in a sentence.

Instrucciones: Encierra con un círculo cada adjetivo en las oraciones. Luego, subraya el sustantivo al que describe. Puede haber más de un adjetivo en una oración.

1. The (beautiful) <u>sailboat</u> is in the lake.

2. The big sail blows in the cool wind.

3. The hot sun feels good to the excited kids.

4. The fast boat speeds across the blue water.

5. The happy kids love the ride.

Use two adjectives to describe something you like.

Usa dos adjetivos para describir algo que te gusta.

#13534—*Kids Learn! Getting Ready for 2nd Grade* © *Teacher Created Materials*

Longest to Shortest

Directions: Number the pictures 1 to 3, from longest to shortest.

Instrucciones: Enumera las imágenes del 1 al 3, del más largo al más corto.

1.

__2__   __1__   __3__

4.

____   ____   ____

2.

____   ____   ____

5.

____   ____   ____

3.

____   ____   ____

6.

____   ____   ____

Talk About It!
¡Hablar de ello!

Which is the longest object?

¿Cuál es el objeto más largo?

Farmer Gray's Morning

Directions: Read the passage, then answer the questions.

Instrucciones: Lee el pasaje, luego contesta las preguntas.

Farmer Gray woke as the sun came up. He had a lot of work to do. He went outside and looked at the sky. A storm was coming. He knew he had to hurry.

So, he went to the barn and fed the horses. He cleaned the pigpen. He collected the eggs from the henhouse. Then, he checked on the cows in the pasture.

Soon, the sky grew dark. It started to rain. He ran back to the house. In the kitchen, he smelled eggs and bacon cooking. All that work, and the day had just begun!

1. What is the setting of this passage?

   _____

2. What are three places you could see on this farm?

   _____

What time of day is it in the passage? How do you know?

¿Qué hora del día es en el pasaje? ¿Cómo sabes?

Shape Subtraction

Directions: Write subtraction number sentences by choosing one number from each shape below. Then, show each problem on the number line.

Instrucciones: Escribe oraciones numéricas de restas al escoger un número de cada figura de abajo. Luego, muestra cada problema en la línea numérica.

7   15   9   12
8   6   11

1   4   2   3
0   5   6

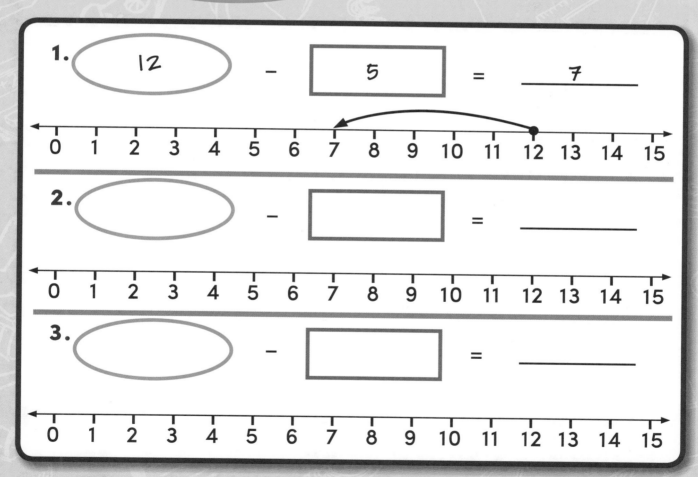

1. (12) − [5] = ___7___

2. ( ) − [ ] = _____

3. ( ) − [ ] = _____

Talk About It! ¡Hablar de ello!
What is the related addition fact for each number sentence you wrote?
¿Cuál es la operación de suma relacionada a cada oración numérica que escribiste?

Draw the Picture!

Directions: Draw pictures to show the meanings of the sentences.

Instrucciones: *Haz dibujos para mostrar los significados de las oraciones.*

1. One of the balloons popped. It was not the same color as the others.	
2. The rectangle is larger than the square.	
3. One of the candles has been blown out.	
4. Two of the balls are different.	

Tell your parent a short story. Ask your parent to draw a picture for your story.

Cuéntale a uno de tus padres un cuento corto. Pídele a uno de tus padres que haga un dibujo para tu cuento.

Write the Hour

Directions: Write the time shown on each clock.

Instrucciones: Escribe la hora que se muestra en cada reloj.

1.

3:00

4.

1:00

2.

7:30

5.

5:00

3.

9:30

6.

10:00

Talk About It!
¡Hablar de ello!

Which hand shows the hour and which hand shows the minutes?

¿Cuál manecilla muestra la hora y cuál manecilla muestra los minutos?

Book Report

Directions: Read a fictional book. Then, write about the book.

Instrucciones: Lee un libro de ficción. Luego, escribe acerca del libro.

Title: _____

Characters: _____

Setting: _____

Retell The Story: _____

_____

_____

_____

_____

_____

_____

_____

#13534—*Kids Learn! Getting Ready for 2nd Grade* © *Teacher Created Materials*

Beginning Sounds

Directions: Circle the beginning sound for each picture.

Instrucciones: Encierra con un círculo el sonido inicial de cada imagen.

1. th (wh)

2. (ch) sh

3. (ch) sh

4. ch (sh)

5. th (wh)

6. ch (sh)

7. (th) wh

8. (ch) sh

Talk About It!
¡Hablar de ello!

Name a word that ends with *sh*.

Nombra una palabra que termina con sh.

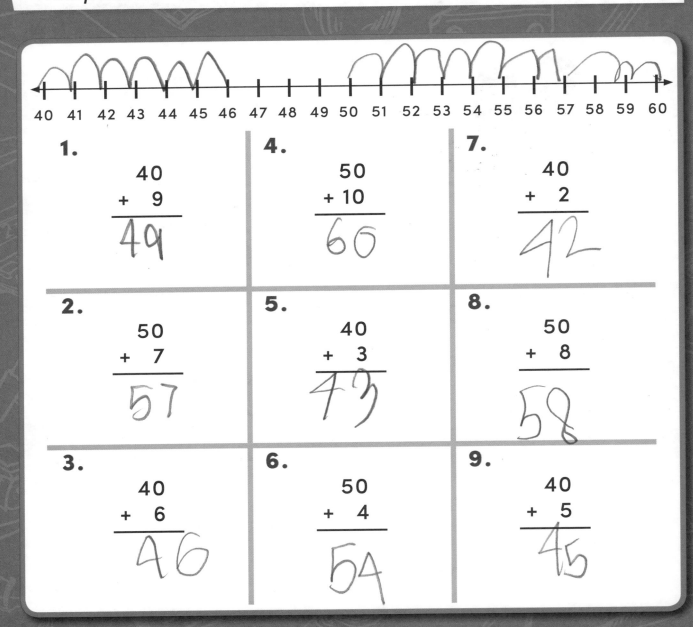

Big Addition Problems!

Directions: Use the number line to solve the problems.

Instrucciones: *Usa la línea numérica para resolver los problemas.*

1.
```
  40
+  9
----
 49
```

2.
```
  50
+  7
----
 57
```

3.
```
  40
+  6
----
 46
```

4.
```
  50
+ 10
----
 60
```

5.
```
  40
+  3
----
 43
```

6.
```
  50
+  4
----
 54
```

7.
```
  40
+  2
----
 42
```

8.
```
  50
+  8
----
 58
```

9.
```
  40
+  5
----
 45
```

Talk About It! **¡Hablar de ello!**

How could you solve the problems without the number line?

¿Cómo podrías resolver los problemas sin la línea numérica?

A Trip to the Store

Directions: Read the passage, then answer the questions.

Instrucciones: Lee el pasaje, luego contesta las preguntas.

"We are out of milk," said Dad.

"Let's go to the store to get some," said Marty.

Dad and Marty got into the car. Dad could not start the car. "I left my keys in the house," said Dad.

Dad and Marty got out of the car and went back to the house. The door would not open. "I locked the door," said Dad. "Now we can't get into the house."

"The kitchen window is open," said Marty. "I can fit in."

Dad lifted Marty through the window. Marty found his dad's keys and walked out the front door. Finally! Dad and Marty were on their way to the store. Now, what did they need again?

1. Where are Dad and Marty going?
   - (A) to the store
   - (B) to the mall
   - (C) to the park
   - (D) to the movies

2. Why won't the car start?
   - (A) It is out of gas.
   - (B) Dad doesn't have the car keys.
   - (C) It is locked.
   - (D) It has a flat tire.

**Talk About It!
¡Hablar de ello!**

Where in the passage did you find the answer to each question?
¿Dónde en el pasaje encontraste la respuesta a cada pregunta?

Sort These

Directions: Answer the questions.

Instrucciones: Contesta las preguntas.

1. How many things that move on <u>land</u> are shown?

   _____

2. How many things that move in the <u>air</u> are shown?

   _____

3. How many things that move in the <u>water</u> are shown?

   _____

Name one other vehicle that belongs in each category.

Nombra otro vehículo que pertenezca a cada categoría.

Pronouns at Work

Directions: Replace the underlined noun or nouns with a pronoun from the Word Bank.

Instrucciones: Reemplaza el sustantivo o sustantivos subrayados con un pronombre del Banco de palabras.

Word Bank

He   She   him   They

1. <u>Mom and José</u> went to the mall.

   They went to the mall.

2. <u>Mom</u> got a new coat.

   _____

3. <u>José</u> wanted to look at games.

   _____

4. José saw his friend. He waved at <u>Sam</u>.

   _____

Which pronoun do you use when you talk about yourself?

¿Cuál pronombre usas cuando hablas sobre ti mismo?

Create New Shapes

Directions: Put the shapes together to make new shapes.

Instrucciones: *Junta las figuras para formar nuevas figuras.*

Shapes	New Shape
1.	
2.	
3.	
4.	

All About Horses

Directions: Read the passage, then retell it in your own words. *Hint:* You may want to cover up the passage when you write your summary.

Instrucciones: *Lee el pasaje, luego cuéntalo en tus propias palabras. Pista: Quizá quieras cubrir el pasaje cuando escribas tu resumen.*

Horses live all over the world. In the wild, they live on plains. With people, they may live in fields, stables, and corrals.

Horses are active. So, they are big eaters. They eat plants. They like grasses and grains. They like sweet treats, such as apples. They like sugar cubes, too.

A *stallion* is a male horse. A female horse is called a *mare*. Horse babies are *colts* if they are males. They are *fillies* if they are female. All horse babies are called *foals*.

_____

_____

_____

_____

Talk About It! ¡Hablar de ello!

Tell what this passage is about using only one word.
Di sobre qué se trata este pasaje usando sólo una palabra.

Line Them Up!

Directions: Write the numbers in order from least to greatest.

Instrucciones: Escribe los números en orden de menor a mayor.

1.

92
16   21
41   12

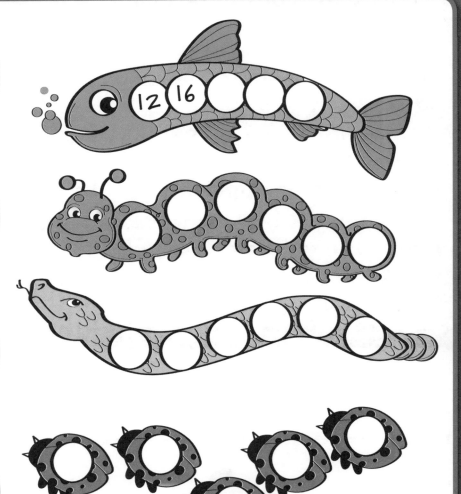

12   16

2.

33
86
73   50
13
37

3.

47   81
40   7
14
74

4.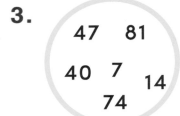

81
30   56   19
99

Complete the Sentence

Directions: Complete each sentence using a word from the Word Bank.

Instrucciones: Completa cada oración usando una palabra del Banco de palabras.

Word Bank

blue   the   put   can   is   said

1. We _____put_____ up a tent at our camp.

2. The sky is big and _____.

3. I _____ count to one hundred.

4. The sun _____ bright today.

5. I got wet in _____ rain.

6. Mom _____ I could have a cookie.

Talk About It!
¡Hablar de ello!

How do you spell each of the words from the Word Bank? No peeking!

¿Cómo se deletrea cada palabra del Banco de palabras? ¡Sin ver!

Wh...

Subtraction Word Problems

Directions: Solve each subtraction problem. Choose the correct answer.

Instrucciones: Resuelve cada problema de resta. Escoge la respuesta correcta.

1. Jill had 5 cookies. She ate 2 cookies. How many cookies does she have left?

- (A) 7
- (B) 3
- (C) 4
- (D) 2

3. An apple tree has 10 apples. Kim picked 2 apples. Michelle picked 3 apples. How many apples are left on the tree?

- (A) 8
- (B) 6
- (C) 7
- (D) 5

2. Soo Yi had 6 candy bars. He ate 1 candy bar. How many candy bars does he have left?

- (A) 5
- (B) 7
- (C) 4
- (D) 8

4. Jack started with 6 cherries. He ate 1 in the morning, and 2 in the evening. How many cherries are left?

- (A) 5
- (B) 4
- (C) 3
- (D) 2

Talk About It!
¡Hablar de ello!

What number sentence could you write for problem 4?

¿Qué oración numérica podrías escribir para el problema 4?

What Makes a Good Friend?

Directions: Write your opinion about what makes a good friend.

Instrucciones: Escribe tu opinión sobre lo que es un buen amigo.

how to make a good
friend is to make
them happy. Is
also by playing with
them. That is how
you make a good
friend.

Put It Together

Directions: Fill in each blank with a conjunction from the Word Bank.

Instrucciones: *Completa cada espacio en blanco con una conjunción del Banco de palabras.*

Conjunctions join words or phrases together. Conjunctions are words such as *and, because, but, or,* and *so.*

Las conjunciones unen palabras o frases. Conjunciones son palabras como and, because, but, or *y* so.

Word Bank

and   because   but   or

1. The game ended _____because_____ of the rain.

2. I like art _____and_____ math.

3. Mom said I could play, _____but_____ I had to do my homework first.

4. Either pizza _____or_____ chicken would be fine with me.

Make up a sentence using the conjunction *and.*

Crea una oración usando la conjunción and.

Put These Together

Directions: Join the sentences to make a compound sentence. *Hint:* Use a conjunction such as *and*, *but*, or *or*.

Instrucciones: *Une las oraciones para formar una oración compuesta. Pista: Usa una conjunción como* and, but, *o* or.

1. I like playing soccer. I like watching soccer.

_____

_____

2. I went to bed. I dreamed all night.

_____

_____

3. Do you like dogs? Do you like cats?

_____

_____

Which conjunctions did you use to combine the sentences?

¿Cuáles conjunciones usaste para unir las oraciones?

The Living Forest

Directions: Read the passage, then answer the questions.

Instrucciones: Lee el pasaje, luego contesta las preguntas.

The forest is home to many living things, big and small.

In the forest there are plants. There are trees growing big and tall. There are flowers growing bright and small. There are grasses thick and green.

In the forest there are lots of animals. There are big animals like bears and deer. There are animals that fly, like owls and eagles. There are even animals that smell, like skunks. Pee-uuww!

In the forest there is water. There are rivers with fish. There are ponds with frogs and turtles.

The forest is alive with many amazing living things.

1. What is the forest home to?
   - (A) people
   - (B) living things
   - (C) cars
   - (D) fields

2. Which flying animal is in the passage?
   - (A) eagle
   - (B) flamingo
   - (C) parrot
   - (D) turtle

Talk About It!
¡Hablar de ello!

Where in the passage did you find the answer to each question?

¿Dónde en el pasaje encontraste la respuesta a cada pregunta?

Hand Measures

Directions: Estimate the number of your hand-lengths each object is. Then, use your hand to measure the length of each object.

Instrucciones: Calcula el número de manos que mide cada objeto. Luego, usa tu mano para medir la longitud de cada objeto.

Object	Estimate	Actual
1. chair	_____ hands	_____ hands
2. table	_____ hands	_____ hands
3. window	_____ hands	_____ hands
4. refrigerator	_____ hands	_____ hands
5. bed	_____ hands	_____ hands

¡Talk About It!
¡Hablar de ello!
How would the measurement be different if you used your parent's hand?
¿Cómo cambiaría la medida si usaras la mano de uno de tus padres?

Naming More Nouns

Directions: Decide whether each word is a common or a proper noun. Cross out the letter in the correct column. Use the letters that remain to solve the riddle.

Instrucciones: Decide si cada palabra es un sustantivo común o propio. Tacha la palabra en la columna correcta. Usa las letras que quedan para resolver la adivinanza.

		Proper Noun	Common Noun
1.	Maria	b	a
2.	girl	m	n
3.	month	u	v
4.	California	r	s
5.	state	h	l
6.	Main Street Mall	q	r
7.	Mrs. Chase	b	o
8.	doctor	o	p
9.	lake	m	l

Riddle: What room is not part of a house or building?

a ___ ___ ___ ___ ___ ___ ___ ___ ___
1   2   3   4   5   6   7   8   9

Is your name a common noun or a proper noun?

¿Tu nombre es un sustantivo común o un sustantivo propio?

Addition Word Problems

Directions: Write the numbers to make an addition number sentence. Then, find the answer to each problem.

Instrucciones: Escribe los números para hacer una oración numérica de sumas. Luego, encuentra la respuesta a cada problema.

1. Duke had 5 dog bones. Kim gave him 3 more. Diego gave him 12 more. How many dog bones does Duke have now?

    __5__ + __3__ + __12__ = __20__ dog bones

2. Fluffy had 13 cat toys. Sam gave her 2 more. Kiara gave her 7 more. How many toys does she have now?

    __13__ + __2__ + __7__ = __22__ toys

3. Jack had 5 stickers. His dad gave him 16 more. His brother gave him 6 more. How many stickers does he have now?

    __5__ + __16__ + __6__ = __27__ stickers

4. Mom had 8 hats. Sue gave her 3 more. Ali gave her 14 more. How many does she have now?

    __8__ + __3__ + __14__ = __25__ hats

Talk About It!
¡Hablar de ello!

How do you know when to add?

¿Cómo sabes cuándo sumar?

Words in Action

Directions: Rewrite each sentence to show past tense. *Hint:* The words that are underlined need to be changed.

Instrucciones: Reescribe cada oración para mostrar el tiempo pasado. Pista: Debes cambiar las palabras subrayadas.

1. Jack <u>will</u> <u>go</u> to the farm.

   Jack went to the farm.

2. Jack <u>packs</u> a bag with books and snacks for the ride.

   _____

3. Jack <u>will ride</u> a pony.

   _____

4. He <u>sees</u> a cow in the barn.

   _____

5. He <u>has</u> a lot of fun.

   _____

Talk About It!
¡Hablar de ello!

Tell about something you did yesterday. Use past-tense verbs.

Cuenta sobre algo que hiciste ayer. Usa verbos en el tiempo pasado.

One Way to Compare Numbers

Directions: Write each number. Then, compare the numbers using >, <, or =.

Instrucciones: Escribe cada número. Luego, compara los números usando >, <, o =.

1. 1 ten and 9 ones   (>)   1 ten and 3 ones

   19   13

2. 1 ten and 7 ones   (<)   1 ten and 5 ones

   17   15

3. 1 ten and 0 ones   (<)   1 ten and 8 ones

   10   1·8

4. 1 ten and 1 one   (<)   1 ten and 2 ones

   11   12

5. 1 ten and 6 ones   (>)   1 ten and 3 ones

   10   13

Talk About It!
¡Hablar de ello!

How did you decide which number is greater?

¿Cómo decidiste cuál número es más grande?

Circle the Vowels

Directions: Circle the vowels in each word. Then, circle the number of syllables the word has. *Hint: Every syllable has at least one vowel.*

Instrucciones: *Encierra con un círculo las vocales en cada palabra. Luego, encierra con un círculo el número de sílabas que tiene la palabra. Pista: Cada sílaba tiene al menos una vocal.*

1.		sock	1	2	(3)
2.		wagon	1	2	(3)
3.		lamp	(1)	2	3
4.		triangle	1	2	(3)
5.		spider	1	(2)	3

Talk About It! ¡Hablar de ello!

Name a word with two syllables.
Nombra una palabra con dos sílabas.

#13534—Kids Learn! Getting Ready for 2nd Grade

Subtract Tens

Directions: Solve the problems.

Instrucciones: Resuelve los problemas.

1. 23 – 10

4. 44 – 10

7. 92 – 10

2. 68 – 10

5. 81 – 10

8. 52 – 10

3. 29 – 10

6. 36 – 10

9. 18 – 10

Talk About It!
¡Hablar de ello!

What happens to the tens place of a number when you subtract ten?

¿Qué le ocurre al lugar de las decenas de un número cuando le restas diez?

How To...

Directions: Choose something you know how to do, such as make toast. Write about how to do that.

Instrucciones: Escoge algo que sabes hacer, como hacer pan tostado. Escribe sobre cómo hacerlo.

Base Words and Endings

Directions: Underline each base word. Circle each ending.

Instrucciones: Subraya cada base de palabra. Encierra con un círculo cada terminación.

1.

write(s)

2.

standing

3.

helps

4.

reading

5.

finds

6.

looked

What are the three different word endings on this page?

¿Cuáles son las tres diferentes terminaciones en esta página?

True or Not True?

Directions: Cross out the sentences that are not true.
Hint: There could be more than one.

Instrucciones: *Tacha las oraciones que no son verdaderas.* Pista: *Puede haber dos cosas que no son verdaderas.*

1.	I have a line that curves. I have a straight line. I have parallel sides. ✗
2.	I have 4 sides. I have 2 sets of parallel sides. ✗ I have a line that curves. Two sides are longer. Three sides are shorter.
3.	I have 4 sides. I have 2 sets of parallel sides. There are 2 sides that are longer.
4.	I have parallel sides. I have a side that curves.
5.	I have 3 sides. There are 2 sides that are parallel.

Make up one true sentence and one false sentence about a pentagon.
Crea una oración verdadera y una oración falsa sobre un pentágono.

#13534—*Kids Learn! Getting Ready for 2nd Grade*   © *Teacher Created Materials*

Buzzing Bees

Directions: Read the passage, then answer the questions.

Instrucciones: Lee el pasaje, luego contesta las preguntas.

Two girls stepped out into the backyard. The air was hot, but the pool looked cool and refreshing. The girls were ready to jump in for a swim.

Just then, a swarm of bees flew near. The girls ducked their heads. They ran around the picnic table on the grass. The bees still buzzed around. Finally, the girls ran inside the house.

Just then, the girls heard a swishing sound. The sprinklers came on. The bees flew away. Finally, the girls could go in the cool pool.

1. What was the girls' problem?
   - (A) the sprinklers
   - (B) the pool
   - (C) the picnic table
   - (D) the buzzing bees

2. What made the swishing sound?
   - (A) the bees
   - (B) the sprinklers
   - (C) the pool
   - (D) the girls

Talk About It! ¡Hablar de ello!

Where in the passage did you find the answer to each question?

¿Dónde en el pasaje encontraste la respuesta a cada pregunta?

Skip Backwards

Directions: Solve the problems. Use the number line.

Instrucciones: Resuelve los problemas. Usa la línea numérica.

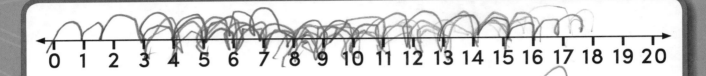

0 1 2 3 4 5 6 7 8 9 10 11 12 13 14 15 16 17 18 19 20

1. $8 - 3 =$ __5__

2. $12 - 2 =$ __9__

3. $10 - 7 =$ __3__

4. $18 - 5 =$ __13__

5. $11 - 8 =$ __3__

6. $7 - 4 =$ __3__

7. $6 - 6 =$ __0__

8. $15 - 7 =$ __8__

9. $13 - 8 =$ __5__

10. $16 - 7 =$ __8__

Talk About It! ¡Hablar de ello!

How did the number line help you subtract?

¿Cómo te ayudó a restar la línea numérica?

Preposition Play

Directions: Choose a preposition from the Word Bank to complete each sentence.

Instrucciones: Escoje una preposición del Banco de palabras para completar la oración.

A *preposition* connects a noun to other parts of a sentence. Some common prepositions are in the Word Bank below.

Una preposición conecta a un sustantivo con las otras partes de la oración. Algunas preposiciones comunes se encuentran en el Banco de palabras de abajo.

Word Bank

| on | in | out | at | across | beside |

1. We went to town _____ on _____ a bus.

2. We rode _____ town on the bus.

3. I sat _____ a seat.

4. My mom sat _____ me.

5. I wanted to look _____ the window.

6. I looked _____ all the scenery.

Talk About It! ¡Hablar de ello!

Use a preposition to tell where you are right now.

Usa una preposición para decir dónde estás en este momento.

Color Shape Parts

Directions: Follow the steps.

Instrucciones: Sigue los pasos.

1. Divide the square in half. Color one half red. Color the other half green.

2. Divide the rectangle in half. Color one half orange. Color the other half yellow.

3. Divide the circle in half. Color one half brown. Color the other half pink.

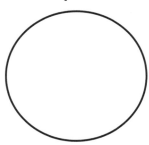

Talk About It!
¡Hablar de ello!

How many parts do you have when you divide a shape in half?

¿Cuántas partes tienes cuando divides una figura por la mitad?

Long-Vowel Review

Directions: Circle the missing word. Write it on the line.

Instrucciones: Encierra con un círculo la palabra que falta. Escríbela en la línea.

1.

She picked a

_____rose_____ for me.

(rose)   ross

2.

Mom will

__bake__ a cake.

back   ~~bake~~

3.

The class stands

in a __line__.

(line)   lyne

4.

That elephant is

__huge__.

(huge)   hug

5.

I __ate__

an apple.

~~ate~~   aet

6.

He is flying a

__kite__.

kit   ~~kite~~

Talk About It! ¡Hablar de ello!

Which letters make the long vowel sound in each word you circled?

¿Cuáles letras hacen el sonido largo de las vocales en cada palabra que circulaste?

True or False?

Directions: Solve the problem. Then, circle to show whether the number sentence is true or false.

Instrucciones: *Resuelve el problema. Luego, encierra con un círculo para mostrar si la oración numérica es verdadera o falsa.*

1. $3 + 4 = 4 + 3$

____7____ = ____7____

(true)   false

2. $5 + 1 = 1 + 4$

_____ = _____

true   false

3. $2 + 2 = 3 + 1$

_____ = _____

true   false

4. $2 + 4 = 3 + 3$

_____ = _____

true   false

5. $3 + 4 = 5 + 1$

_____ = _____

true   false

6. $7 + 1 = 3 + 4$

_____ = _____

true   false

Talk About It!
¡Hablar de ello!

What does the equal sign mean?

¿Qué significa el signo igual?

Read and Rhyme

Directions: Read each word. Circle the picture that rhymes with the word.

Instrucciones: Lee cada palabra. Encierra con un círculo la imagen que rima con la palabra.

1. one		**10**
2. said		
3. were		
4. there		
5. what		
6. their		

Spell the word for each picture you circled.

Deletrea la palabra de la imagen que encerraste con un círculo.

#13534—Kids Learn! Getting Ready for 2nd Grade **83**

Place-Value Practice

Directions: Answer the questions.

Instrucciones: Contesta las preguntas.

1. How many tens are in the number 30?

   _____

2. How many ones are in the number 42?

   _____

3. How many ones are in the number 26?

   _____

4. How many tens are in the number 85?

   _____

5. How many ones are in the number 91?

   _____

6. How many ones are in the number 73?

   _____

7. How many tens are in the number 69?

   _____

8. How many tens are in the number 46?

   _____

9. How many ones are in the number 82?

   _____

10. How many tens are in the number 47?

    _____

How do you know where the tens place is in a number?

¿Cómo sabes dónde está el lugar de las decenas en un número?

The Best Gift

Directions: Write about the best gift you ever received.

Instrucciones: Escribe sobre el mejor regalo que hayas recibido.

Great Work!

_____

(Name)

has completed

Kids Learn! Getting Ready for 2nd Grade

_____

(Date)

Extra Activities
Actividades extra

Dear Friend

Directions: Write a letter to your friend. Explain why he or she should come play at your house. Write your letter on a separate sheet of paper. Be sure to include all the parts of a friendly letter. See the example below.

Instrucciones: Escribe una carta a tu amigo. Explica por qué debería venir a jugar a tu casa. Escribe tu carta en una hoja de papel aparte. Asegúrate de incluir todas las partes de una carta amistosa. Ve el ejemplo a continuación.

Greeting   Date

July 4, 2014

Dear Emily,

We had the best picnic ever today! We ate great food and played at the park all day. After it got dark, there was a beautiful fireworks show. How was your Independence Day?

Closing   Your friend,

Andre

Signature

Transportation Firsts

Directions: Look at the time line. Answer the questions.

Instrucciones: Mira la línea de tiempo. Contesta las preguntas.

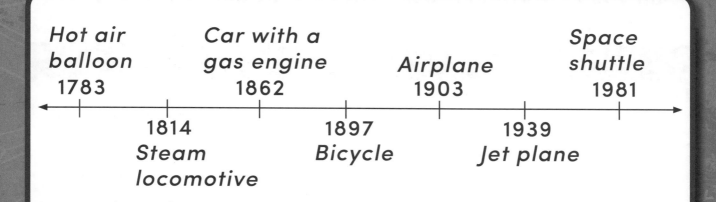

Hot air balloon 1783

Car with a gas engine 1862

Airplane 1903

Space shuttle 1981

1814 Steam locomotive

1897 Bicycle

1939 Jet plane

1. In which year was the airplane invented?

   1903

2. What is the first invention shown on this time line?

   Hot air balloon — 17 83

3. Which invention happened in 1939?

   Jet plane 19_39

4. Which invention is shown just after the steam locomotive on this time line?

   car with a gas engine

5. What is the last invention shown on this time line?

   Space shuttle 19_81

Watch It Grow

Directions: Plant a seed in the ground or in a cup with soil. Watch it grow. Record what you see below. Use more paper, if needed.

Instrucciones: *Siembra una semilla en la tierra o en un vaso. Mírala crecer. Registra abajo lo que ves. Usa más papel si es necesario.*

Day 1 _____

Day 7 _____

Day 14 _____

Day 21 _____

Day 28 _____

Make a Clock

Directions: Cut out the clock. Use a brad to assemble the clock. Use the clock to practice showing times.

Instrucciones: Recorta el reloj. Usa una tachuela para armar el reloj. Usa el reloj para practicar la hora.

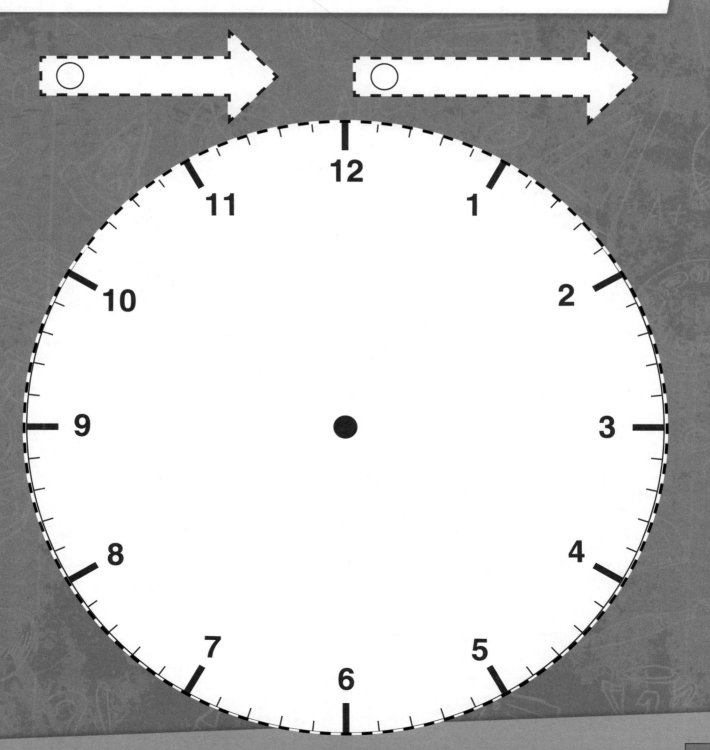

Money, Money

Directions: Cut out the cards below. Write the total value of the coins on each card. Put the cards in order from least to greatest.

Instrucciones: *Recorta las tarjetas de abajo. Escribe el valor del dinero en cada tarjeta. Pon las tarjetas en orden de la menor a la mayor cantidad.*

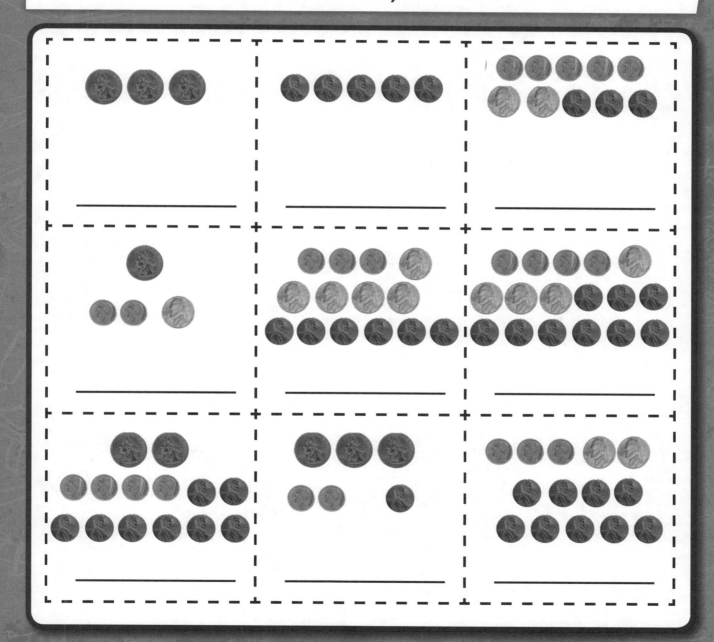

Water Observation

Directions: *Observe water in all three forms. Record what you see.*

Instrucciones: *Observa el agua en sus tres formas. Registra lo que ves.*

1. ***Liquid***—Pour some water into a glass.

_____

_____

2. ***Solid***—Hold a piece of ice.

_____

_____

3. ***Gas***—Look at a pot of boiling water. (Have your parent help you.)

_____

_____

#13534—Kids Learn! Getting Ready for 2nd Grade

97

Branches of Government

Directions: Have a parent help you research the three branches of U.S. Government. Use the Internet or nonfiction books from the library. Take notes on what you learn about each branch. Answer the questions about each branch on another sheet of paper.

Instrucciones: Pídele a uno de tus padres que te ayude a investigar sobre las tres ramas del gobierno de Estados Unidos. Usa la Internet o libros de no ficción de la biblioteca. Toma nota de lo que aprendiste de cada rama. Contesta las preguntas sobre cada rama en otra hoja de papel.

Branch of Government	Questions
 Executive Branch	Who is in it?
 Legislative Branch	What does it do? Where is it?
 Judicial Branch	Why is it important?

Get to Know Your Ancestors

Directions: Your *ancestors* are your family members who lived long ago. Interview a parent or grandparent about your ancestors. Use the questions below to help you.

Instrucciones: Tus ancestros *son miembros de tu familia que vivieron hace mucho tiempo. Entrevista a uno de tus padres o abuelos acerca de tus ancestros. Usa las preguntas de abajo para guiarte.*

1. Where did our ancestors live?

   _____

2. What are some important things our ancestors did?

   _____

3. How did that lead to us living in our hometown?

   _____

Find a Folk Tale

Directions: Read a folk tale. Then, complete this form.

Instrucciones: *Lee una fábula. Luego, llena este formulario.*

Folk tales and fairy tales have some common features.
- The tales are usually short and simple.
- There is a lot of action.
- There is a problem that needs to be solved.
- There is usually a happy ending.

Las fábulas y los cuentos de hadas tienen algunas características en común.
- *Los cuentos son usualmente cortos y sencillos.*
- *Hay mucha acción.*
- *Existe un problema que necesita ser resuelto.*
- *Usualmente hay un final feliz.*

Title: _____

Author (if known): _____

Setting: _____

Hero or Heroes: _____

Problem: _____

Lesson Learned: _____

Addition Facts within Ten

Directions: Cut out the flashcards. Use them to memorize addition facts within ten.

Instrucciones: Recorta las tarjetas ilustrativas. Úsalas para memorizar las operaciones de sumas en diez.

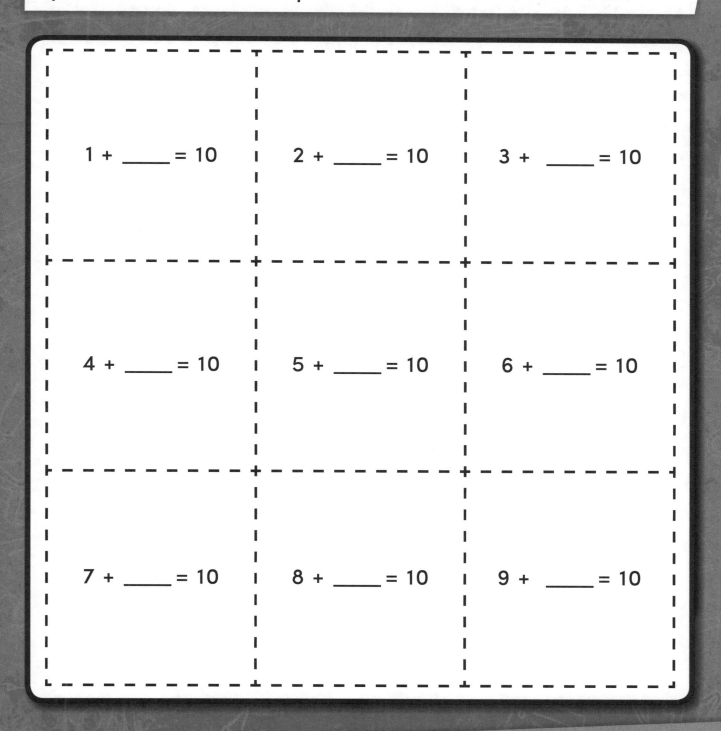

1 + _____ = 10

2 + _____ = 10

3 + _____ = 10

4 + _____ = 10

5 + _____ = 10

6 + _____ = 10

7 + _____ = 10

8 + _____ = 10

9 + _____ = 10

7	8	9
4	5	6
1	2	3

#13534—Kids Learn! Getting Ready for 2nd Grade

© *Teacher Created Materials*

Ten Frame and Counters

Directions: Cut out the counters. Place them in the Ten Frame to show the addition facts on page 101. Use a different color counter for each number that you add together to make 10.

Instrucciones: Corta las fichas. Colócalas en el cuadro de diez para mostrar las operaciones de sumas en la página 101. Usa una ficha de color diferente para cada número que sumas para llegar a diez.

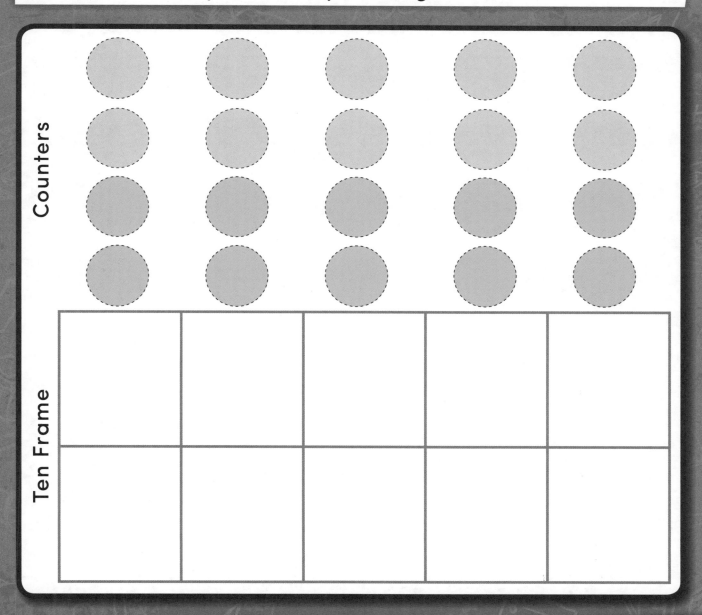

Counters

Ten Frame

Answer Key

Page 20
1. long
2. short
3. long
4. long
5. long
6. long
7. long
8. short
9. short

Talk About It: Answers will vary.

Page 21
1. 104, 105, 106, 107, 108, 109, 110, 111
2. 98, 99, 100, 102, 103, 104, 105, 106
3. 116, 118, 119, 120, 121, 122, 123, 124
4. 115, 116, 117, 118, 120, 121, 122, 123
5. 105, 106, 108, 109, 110, 111, 112, 113
6. 110, 111, 113, 114, 115, 116, 117, 118

Talk About It: Answers will vary.

Page 22
1. B
2. B

Talk About It:
1. Things to do at the beach: sit on the sand, read a book, build sandcastles, use sand shovels and pails, pick up seashells and sand dollars, play in the water, surfing.
2. They use sand, shovels, and pails.

Page 23
1. >
2. <
3. >
4. <
5. =
6. >
7. <
8. <

Talk About It: 100

Page 24
1. trees
2. cat
3. stars
4. pen
5. books
6. ball

Sentences will vary but should use a word from the activity.

Talk About It: trees, stars, books

Page 25
1. one whole
2. one-half
3. one-quarter
4. one-third

Talk About It: Answers will vary. The number of equal parts and the number of shaded parts determine the fraction.

Page 26
1. !
2. .
3. .
4. !
5. .
6. ?
7. !
8. ?

Talk About It: Answers will vary.

Page 27
Children should have drawn 2 hot dogs on Jamie's plate, 2 hot dogs on Jackson's plate, and one hot dog on Dad's plate. There are 5 hot dogs in all.

Talk About It: $2 + 2 + 1 = 5$

Page 28
1. mitten
2. ladder
3. flower
4. lemon
5. rabbit

Talk About It: 2 syllables

Page 29
1. 6
2. 7
3. 5
4. 2
5. 10
6. 3
7. 8
8. 1

Talk About It: Answers will vary.

Page 30
Answers will vary.

Page 31
1. cub
2. tub
3. kit
4. can
5. cube
6. tube
7. kite
8. cane

Talk About It: letter e

Page 32

1. B
2. C
3. B
4. C
5. A
6. B
7. C
8. B

Talk About It: Answers will vary. Possible answer: Look at the tens place and then the ones place.

Page 33

1. 15
2. 16
3. 11
4. 14
5. 1 ten, 9 ones
6. 1 ten, 3 ones
7. 1 ten, 8 ones

Talk About It: 20 ones.

Page 34

1. 24, 44
2. 9, 29
3. 16, 36
4. 29, 49
5. 11, 31
6. 30, 50
7. 0, 20
8. 25, 45

Talk About It: Answers will vary.

Page 35

Tools or Things Used at Work: computer, desk, hammer, mop, ruler, saw
Workers: dancer, farmer, pilot, teacher, doctor, writer

Talk About It: Answers will vary.

Page 36

1. $16 - 10 = 6$
2. $11 - 1 = 10$
3. $13 - 5 = 8$
4. $10 - 3 = 7$

Talk About It: Answers will vary.

Page 37

1. Tracy
2. Answers will vary. Accept any reasonable answer such as: excited, prepared, etc.

Talk About It: Answers will vary.

Page 38

Answers will vary.

Talk About It: Answers will vary.

Page 39

1. talked, talks, talking
2. stayed, stays, staying
3. boxed, boxing, boxes
4. fished, fishing, fishes
5. started, starts, starting

Talk About It: Children should read the words.

Page 40

1. 2
2. 10
3. 1
4. 10
5. 7
6. 5
7. 9
8. 10

Talk About It: Answers will vary. Possible answer:
Look at the answer on the other side of the equal sign. Add if the number is larger. Subtract if the number is smaller.

Page 41

Answers will vary.

Page 42

1. Jan (short), Jane (long)
2. plan (short), plane (long)
3. note (long), not (short)
4. pin (short), pine (long)
5. pan (short), pane (long)

Talk About It: It is silent.

Page 43

1. 2 tens, 0 ones
2. 7 tens, 9 ones
3. 4 tens, 5 ones
4. 3 tens, 8 ones
5. 6 tens, 1 one

Talk About It: 90; Answers will vary.

Page 44

1. B
2. B

Talk About It:

1. A tadpole looks like a little fish.
2. Then the cycle starts again.

Page 45

1. $9 + 6 = 15$; $15 - 6 = 9$
2. $5 + 8 = 13$; $13 - 8 = 5$
3. $3 + 4 = 7$; $7 - 4 = 3$
4. $9 + 7 = 16$; $16 - 7 = 9$

Talk About It: The fact family is a double.

Answer Key (cont.)

Page 46

1. (beautiful) sailboat
2. (big) sail, (cool) wind
3. (hot) sun, (excited) kids
4. (fast) boat, (blue) water
5. (happy) kids

Talk About It: Answers will vary.

Page 47

1. 2, 1, 3
2. 2, 1, 3
3. 3, 1, 2
4. 3, 2, 1
5. 2, 1, 3
6. 3, 1, 2

Talk About It: house

Page 48

1. a farm
2. Answers may vary: barn, pigpen, henhouse, pasture, house/kitchen

Talk About It: It is morning; the sun just came up and the farmer just woke up.

Page 49

Answers will vary.

Talk About It: Answers will vary.

Page 50

Check to be sure student pictures matched the sentences.

1. Several balloons are colored the same color. One balloon should be colored a different color.
2. There is a large rectangle and a small square.
3. Several candles that are lit. One candle is not lit.
4. Several balls that are the same. Two balls are different.

Talk About It: Answers will vary.

Page 51

1. 3:00
2. 6:30
3. 9:30
4. 1:00
5. 5:00
6. 10:00

Talk About It: The shorter hand is the hour hand. The longer hand is the minute hand.

Page 52

Answers will vary.

Page 53

1. wh
2. ch
3. ch
4. sh
5. wh
6. sh
7. th
8. ch

Talk About It: Answers will vary.

Page 54

1. 49
2. 57
3. 46
4. 60
5. 43
6. 54
7. 42
8. 58
9. 45

Talk About It: Answers will vary.

Page 55

1. A
2. B

Talk About It:

1. "Let's go to the store to get some," said Marty.
2. Dad could not start the car. "I left my keys in the house," said Dad.

Page 56

1. 3
2. 2
3. 2

Talk About It: Answers will vary.

Page 57

1. They
2. She
3. He
4. him

Talk About It: I

Page 58

Answers will vary. Possible answers:

1.
2.
3.
4.

Talk About It: Answers will vary.

Page 59

Answers will vary.

Talk About It: horses

Page 60

1. 12, 16, 21, 41, 92
2. 13, 33, 37, 50, 73, 86
3. 7, 14, 40, 47, 74, 81
4. 19, 30, 56, 81, 99

Talk About It: 99; Answers will vary.

Answer Key (cont.)

Page 61

1. put
2. blue
3. can
4. is
5. the
6. said

Talk About It: blue, the, put, can, is, said

Page 62

1. B
2. A
3. D
4. C

Talk About It: $6 - 1 - 2 = 3$

Page 63

Answers will vary.

Page 64

1. because
2. and
3. but
4. or

Talk About It: Answers will vary.

Page 65

1. I like playing and watching soccer.
2. I went to bed and dreamed all night.
3. Do you like dogs or cats?

Talk About It: Responses will vary, but may include *and* and *or*.

Page 66

1. B
2. A

Talk About It:

1. The forest is home to many living things, big and small.
2. There are animals that fly, like owls and eagles.

Page 67

Answers will vary.

Talk About It: The measurements would be smaller with a larger hand.

Page 68

1. proper noun
2. common noun
3. common noun
4. proper noun
5. common noun
6. proper noun
7. proper noun
8. common noun
9. common noun

Riddle: a mushroom

Talk About It: proper noun

Page 69

1. $5 + 3 + 12 = 20$
2. $13 + 2 + 7 = 22$
3. $5 + 16 + 6 = 27$
4. $8 + 3 + 14 = 25$

Talk About It: Add when things are being put together.

Page 70

1. went
2. packed
3. rode
4. saw
5. had

Talk About It: Answers will vary.

Page 71

1. $19 > 13$
2. $17 > 15$
3. $10 < 18$
4. $11 < 12$
5. $16 > 13$

Talk About It: The greater number has more ones.

Page 72

1. s(o)ck; 1
2. wag(o)n; 2
3. l(a)mp; 1
4. tr(i)(a)ngl(e); 3
5. sp(i)d(e)r; 2

Talk About It: Answers will vary.

Page 73

1. 13
2. 58
3. 19
4. 34
5. 71
6. 26
7. 82
8. 42
9. 8

Talk About It: The number in the tens places gets smaller by one.

Page 74

Answers will vary.

Page 75

1. write(s)
2. stand(ing)
3. help(s)
4. read(ing)
5. find(s)
6. look(ed)

Talk About It: *-s*, *-ed*, and *-ing*

Answer Key (cont.)

Page 76

1. Not true: I have parallel sides.
2. Not true: I have a line that curves; Three sides are shorter.
3. Not true: There are 2 sides that are longer.
4. Not true: I have parallel sides.
5. Not true: There are 2 sides that are parallel.

Talk About It: Answers will vary.

Page 77

1. D
2. B

Talk About It:

1. Just then, a swarm of bees flew near. The bees still buzzed around.
2. Just then, the girls heard a swishing sound. The sprinklers came on.

Page 78

1. 5
2. 10
3. 3
4. 13
5. 3
6. 3
7. 0
8. 8
9. 5
10. 9

Talk About It: You can count backward on the number line.

Page 79

1. on
2. across
3. in
4. beside
5. out
6. at

Talk About It: Answers will vary.

Page 80

Answers may vary.

1.
2.
3.

Talk About It: 2 parts

Page 81

1. rose
2. bake
3. line
4. huge
5. ate
6. kite

Talk About It:

1. o and silent e
2. a and silent e
3. i and silent e
4. u and silent e
5. a and silent e
6. i and silent e

Page 82

1. 7, 7, true
2. 6, 5, false
3. 4, 4, true
4. 6, 6, true
5. 7, 6, false
6. 8, 7, false

Talk About It: The equal sign shows the value is the same on both sides.

Page 83

1. sun
2. bed
3. stir
4. bear
5. hut
6. hair

Talk About It: sun, bed, stir, bear, hut, hair

Page 84

1. 3
2. 2
3. 6
4. 8
5. 1
6. 3
7. 6
8. 4
9. 2
10. 4

Talk About It: The tens place is just to the left of the ones place or the second digit from the right.

Page 85

Answers will vary.

Page 90

Answers will vary.

Page 91

1. 1903
2. hot air balloon
3. jet plane
4. car with a gas engine
5. space shuttle

Page 92

Answers will vary.

Answer Key (cont.)

Page 95

● ● ● 75¢	● ● ● ● ● 5¢	● ● ● ● ● ● ● ● ● ● ● ● ● 63¢
● ● ● ● ● 50¢	● ● ● ● ● ● ● ● ● ● ● ● ● ● ● 61¢	● 69¢
● ● ● ● ● ● ● ● ● ● ● ● ● ● 98¢	● ● ● ● ● 96¢	● ● ● ● ● ● ● ● ● ● ● ● ● ● 49¢

Least to greatest: 5¢, 49¢, 50¢, 61¢, 63¢, 69¢, 75¢, 96¢, 98¢

Page 97

Answers will vary.

Page 98

Answers will vary.

Page 99

Answers will vary.

Page 100

Answers will vary.

Kids Learn! Parent Survey

Dear Parent,

The activities in this *Kids Learn!* book have helped your child review grade-level skills from the recent school year and get ready for the year ahead. Your feedback on this learning resource is very valuable. Please complete the survey below and return it as directed by your child's teacher or school administrator. Thank you in advance for your input and your time.

Please circle the term that best describes how you feel about this *Kids Learn!* book.

1. The **Introduction** (pages 4–18) gave me good ideas for things to do with my child and offered helpful resources for extended learning.

   Strongly Agree   Agree   Disagree   Strongly Disagree

   Comments: _____

   _____

2. The **Weekly Activities for Students** (pages 20–85) were easy to understand and helped me guide my child to complete the activity sheets. The activities were at an appropriate level of difficulty for my child.

   Strongly Agree   Agree   Disagree   Strongly Disagree

   Comments: _____

   _____

3. The sections of *Kids Learn!* that were particularly helpful or useful for me and my child were: (*Please check all that apply.*)

   ☐ Top 10 Things Your Second Grader Will Need to Know   ☐ Websites and Apps for Parents and Kids

   ☐ Things to Do at Home   ☐ Weekly Activities for Students

   ☐ Things to Do in the Community   ☐ Extra Activities

   ☐ Suggested Vacation Reading and Log

Please provide any additional comments or suggestions about this *Kids Learn!* book.

_____

_____

Kids Learn! Encuesta para los padres

Querido padre de familia:

Las actividades en este libro *Kids Learn!* han ayudado a su hijo a repasar las destrezas de nivel de grado del reciente año escolar y a prepararse para el año siguiente. Sus comentarios sobre este recurso educativo son muy valiosos. Por favor, complete la encuesta a continuación y regrésela como lo indica el maestro o administrador escolar de su hijo. Le agradecemos de antemano por su participación y por su tiempo.

Por favor encierre con un círculo el término que mejor describe su opinión sobre este libro *Kids Learn!*

1. La **Introducción** (páginas 4–18) me dio buenas ideas de cosas que hacer con mi hijo y me ofrecieron recursos útiles para ampliar el aprendizaje.

   Totalmente de acuerdo　　　De acuerdo　　　En desacuerdo　　　Totalmente en desacuerdo

   Comentarios: _____

   _____

2. Las Actividades semanales para los estudiantes (páginas 20–85) eran fáciles de entender y me ayudaron a guiar a mi hijo a completar las hojas de ejercicios. Las actividades eran de un nivel de dificultad adecuado para mi hijo.

   Totalmente de acuerdo　　　De acuerdo　　　En desacuerdo　　　Totalmente en desacuerdo

   Comentarios: _____

   _____

3. Las secciones de *Kids Learn!* que fueron particularmente útiles o nos ayudaron a mí y a mi hijo fueron: *(Por favor marque todas las que sean pertinentes).*

   ☐ Las 10 cosas que su hijo de segundo grado debe saber

   ☐ Cosas para hacer en casa

   ☐ Cosas para hacer en la comunidad

   ☐ Registro de lectura y la lectura sugerida para las vacaciones

   ☐ Páginas web y aplicaciones para padres y niños

   ☐ Actividades semanales para los estudiantes

   ☐ Actividades extra

Por favor proporcione cualquier comentario o sugerencia adicional sobre este libro *Kids Learn!*

_____

#13534—Kids Learn! Getting Ready for 2nd Grade